Smarter Every Day!

Fun picture workbooks to boost your child's learning potential

What's Missing?

B

How to Use This Book

1. Ask your child what the picture is about. (If your child does not recognize the picture, find similar objects, animals, peoples, or places in the surrounding and show them to your child.)
> *Look at this picture. What is this?.*

2. Read question to your child.

3. Once your child answers, turn the page and check the correct answer.
> *Rabbit's one ear is missing. Rabbits have two long ears.*

4. Let your child apply what he/she has observed to his/her everyday life.
> *Let's find what else has two ears.*
> *Dogs have two ears, cats have two ears, and you have two ears, too.*

5. Let your child imagine what the objects, animals, people, or places would be like without the missing element in real life.

Look carefully at the picture below.
Can you find what's missing?

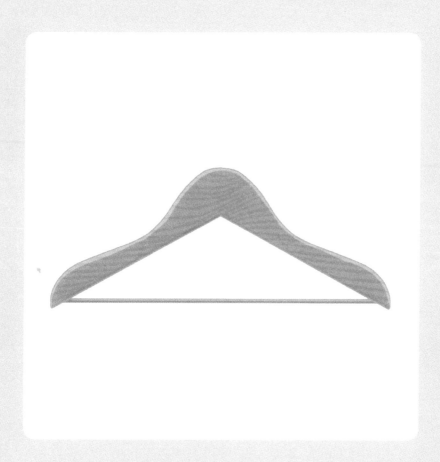

Did you get it right?
Let's check your answer.

Well Done

Look carefully at the picture below.
Can you find what's missing?

Did you get it right?
Let's check your answer.

Look carefully at the picture below.
Can you find what's missing?

Did you get it right?
Let's check your answer.

Well Done

Look carefully at the picture below.
Can you find what's missing?

Did you get it right?
Let's check your answer.

Look carefully at the picture below.
Can you find what's missing?

Did you get it right?
Let's check your answer.

Look carefully at the picture below.
Can you find what's missing?

Did you get it right?
Let's check your answer.

Look carefully at the picture below.
Can you find what's missing?

A12345

Did you get it right?
Let's check your answer.

A12345

Look carefully at the picture below.
Can you find what's missing?

Did you get it right?
Let's check your answer.

Well Done

Look carefully at the picture below.
Can you find what's missing?

Did you get it right?
Let's check your answer.

Well Done

20

Look carefully at the picture below.
Can you find what's missing?

Did you get it right?
Let's check your answer.

Well Done

Look carefully at the picture below.
Can you find what's missing?

Did you get it right?
Let's check your answer.

Look carefully at the picture below.
Can you find what's missing?

Did you get it right?
Let's check your answer.

Well Done

Look carefully at the picture below.
Can you find what's missing?

Did you get it right?
Let's check your answer.

Well Done

Look carefully at the picture below.
Can you find what's missing?

Did you get it right?
Let's check your answer.

Well Done

Look carefully at the picture below.
Can you find what's missing?

Did you get it right?
Let's check your answer.

Well Done

Look carefully at the picture below.
Can you find what's missing?

Did you get it right?
Let's check your answer.

Look carefully at the picture below.
Can you find what's missing?

Did you get it right?
Let's check your answer.

Look carefully at the picture below.
Can you find what's missing?

Did you get it right?
Let's check your answer.

Well Done

38

Look carefully at the picture below.
Can you find what's missing?

Did you get it right?
Let's check your answer.

40

Look carefully at the picture below.
Can you find what's missing?

Did you get it right?
Let's check your answer.

Well Done

Look carefully at the picture below.
Can you find what's missing?

Did you get it right?
Let's check your answer.

44

Look carefully at the picture below.
Can you find what's missing?

Did you get it right?
Let's check your answer.

Well Done

Look carefully at the picture below.
Can you find what's missing?

Did you get it right?
Let's check your answer.

Made in the USA
Middletown, DE
15 November 2019